MONSTERS & GHOSTS
OF WEST VIRGINIA

WHERE TO FIND
MONSTERS & GHOSTS
OF WEST VIRGINIA

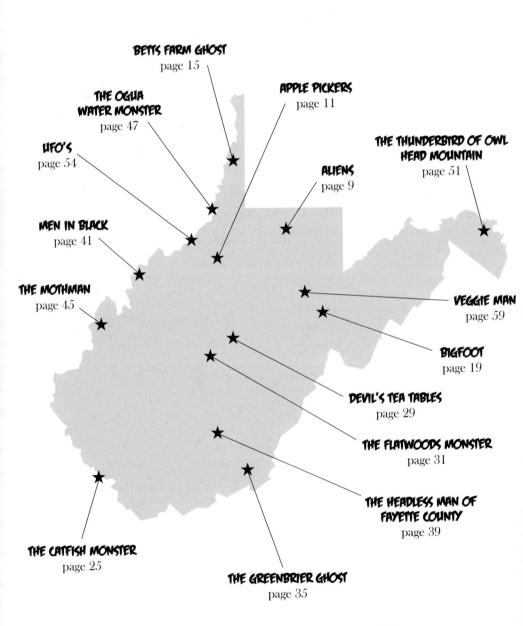

MONSTERS & GHOSTS
OF WEST VIRGINIA

Written by
ERIN TURNER & ISAAC MCKINNON

Illustrated by
ERIN TURNER

quarrier press

Charleston, West Virginia

First Edition

10 9 8 7 6 5 4 3 2

Printed in USA

Library of Congress Control Number: 2011934874
ISBN-13: 978-1-891852-76-3
ISBN-10: 1-891852-76-0

Book and cover design: Mark S. Phillips

Distributed by:

West Virginia Book Company
1125 Central Avenue
Charleston, WV 25302
www.wvbookco.com

TABLE OF CONTENTS

INTRODUCTION

Almost everyone has heard and told ghost and monster stories at some point. As a very young child, a witch in a fairy tale might be your first fictional scary encounter; being afraid of the dark is a common, very real, first scare. Next might be a villain in a Disney movie, or a loud **Boo!** around a sleepy holiday fire. Then maybe we graduate to a camping trip or sleepover without our parents, when the stories might actually start to get scary. Monsters, ghosts, aliens and anything else that is scary and hard or impossible to believe is fun and exciting to talk about.

Passing along ghost stories, or any story, as the listener and the storyteller, is a rite of passage. I grew up in a small town in the hills of Virginia, not that far from the West Virginia border. I have three sisters, lots of stepbrothers and an extended family. We had lots of space, and horses and animals. We spent a lot of time outside. I think the setting lent itself to storytelling, probably more than most.

I was also lucky to spend time each summer on Lake Huron, where we slept in a really cool, old, empty boarding house. At one time local quarry workers had lived in the house. At the farm or the lake house, I would sit with my sisters, family and friends and take turns telling what we had heard about different monsters or ghosts. Then we were left to sort out what we thought was real and what was made up, usually by ourselves, and usually in the dark. This was not just about negotiating the truth about monsters and ghosts, but about understanding the art of storytelling.

My middle school son, Isaac, is at an age where he lives and breathes alien stories and hearing about strange phenomena; he loves all science fiction and comic book monsters. At an earlier age it was dinosaurs, then Star Wars. As he's grown our storytelling time has evolved into watching scary movies or *The Matrix* together, or sharing opinions on the latest mystery we've read.

We both enjoy writing stories, so when our friend Bill suggested this project, I jumped at the chance. What could be more fun than painting monsters and ghosts? And how wonderful to have a writing project that I could work on with Isaac. It was a fun project for both of us. Writing and illustrating stories about common and uncommon West Virginia monsters, we researched all the information we could find. Armed with our notes, names, and dates, Isaac and I began, giving ourselves plenty of artistic license.

We tried to keep the stories fun and in the spirit of the storytelling circle. I had a great time with the monster paintings. We hope you enjoy these stories as much as we did writing them, hopefully giving you material for your next turn around the fire or at bedtime. Maybe you'll even recall one against your will, when you're walking out to the garage in the dark, or spending the night alone in an empty house! **Boo!**

ALIENS

Most of us have looked up into a clear night sky, and wondered if there are other people or creatures out there. Even though we don't have definitive proof of "life on other planets," the question of whether we are alone in the universe is one commonly pondered. Some people firmly believe that there is life on other planets, if not in our solar system, then somewhere beyond.

I think NASA has photographs of what they think is at least frozen algae from one of our space missions. Could that be the beginning of another civilization, or the fragile remains of one long-gone?

I think the majority of "earthlings" aren't sure whether there is life in outer space or not. A select few people say they have seen alien beings for themselves. West Virginia has actually had a relatively high number of reports of close encounters with strange creatures and nightmarish alien abductions.

Are West Virginians more impressionable than most, or more superstitious? Could it be that we spend more time outside at night than in more developed areas, or is it just that our night skies are brighter, and quieter? Do we have a better view here, or is it only that we're subject to an increased power of suggestion? If it's easier to spot a falling star here, could it be easier to imagine some bright lights being a space ship?

APPLE PICKERS

My 12-year old brother George, wide-eyed and out of breath, ran in the house. He was talking so fast we could hardly understand him. He'd seen something frightening in the orchard. He wanted us to hurry back down there with him to see it.

I jumped up ready to go, but Mom told George and I to sit back down. Mom gave George a cold glass of lemonade and told him to catch his breath. "Your father can go down and check around the orchard," she said, giving our dad a nod. Soon Dad had his rifle and headed out the door.

Something had been getting in our orchard, and many others, for years. As far back as we could remember, local farmers had complained about broken branches, torn down fences and the apple trees being stripped of their fruit. It had distressed landowners and spooked school kids for a long time.

There had been a few reports of people seeing a dark, hairy creature, walking upright like a person at the scenes. On occasion, one of these sightings made it into the newspaper. The creatures were dubbed the "Apple Pickers" by some, but the majority just chalked it up to thieves, bears, or vandals.

When Dad returned after finding nothing, George was beside himself. "It was one of those ape-like things! It had thick, dark, red hair and it stank! I'm telling you, you could smell that thing from a mile away, and it ran fast as lightning!" he added.

Mom and Dad rolled their eyes, which made George furious. His face turned red and he stormed out of the room, yelling, "I knew you wouldn't believe me."

But I believed him. George and I had found strange things around the orchard. Last week when we were playing zombie tag I slipped and fell. Right in front of my face was a very large footprint. It could have been the print of a large flatfooted man, but what big guy runs in our woods barefoot?

George and I followed the footprints through the woods a ways. When we paused to look around we noticed hair snagged in some of the heavy brush. The hair was thick and dark red, and it was caught up way high in the ends of the tallest branches. It'd be a stretch to think a bear could be that tall, and the length, smell and odor of the hair didn't resemble any hair of a person or bear we'd ever seen.

A few hunters have set out over the years, determined to find one of these creatures. So far nobody has succeeded. I think they're too smart and too fast to get caught. I know they're out there ... hiding out deep in the mountainous woods. But their weakness for apples will bring them back down. And George and I will be waiting.

BETTS FARM GHOST

Tory had decided. He was going to do it. Every kid in town would look up to him if he did it. He said he would, and he couldn't back down now. He was going to spend the night at the decrepit, scary, abandoned Betts Farm house, in "The Room" that everyone talked about. The room we were almost too scared to talk about, and never dreamed about going into. Sure, Tory had heard horrible things about that house, especially about that room. Everyone agreed it was worse than haunted.

At least once a year some kid would get dared to sleep in it, but they always emerged screaming soon after going in. Some people said that one boy never came back. But Tory didn't believe any of the stories. They had to be fake, like comic books or sci-fi movies.

The story was that a young peddler had come to the Betts' farm over 100 years ago, and was murdered. Supposedly, his spirit never left.

Tory's trance was broken when his alarm went off. It was time. Tory ran downstairs and hollered, "Mom, I'm going to Jack's house!" He ran out the door, grabbed his bike, and rode quickly down the road. He felt more confident every minute. That was, until he could see the house.

Tory's confidence drained from his body, and his legs felt like jelly. It was a horrible house, with dead trees and a rotting broken front porch. The front door didn't shut and the dark empty windows had broken panes. Even from a little distance he could hear it creak and moan with the wind.

Soon after arriving, he noticed all the kids. Tons of them. His friends and enemies, geeks and jocks. It seemed half his middle school was there, all crowded around the house waiting.

"There he is, look!" shouted one of the kids from the house, turning everyone's attention to Tory.

Normally Tory would be staring at the crowd, but not today. Now he looked only at the house. Something was definitely strange about the house, but Tory shook it off. He didn't believe in any of that nonsense, did he?

Alex, a big, tall, beefy boy eyed him intently and greeted him. Alex wasn't fond of Tory, and vice versa.

"So Tory, are you going to wimp out?" Alex sneered while Tory bit his lip.

"I came this far didn't I?" Tory snapped.

Alex spit the next words: "Don't even think about cheating, because we're going to lock you in."

Tory's eyes widened. His tone weakened. "You're going to lock me in?"

"Course we are, otherwise you could just go home when everyone leaves. Calm down, were going to let you out when morning comes," said Alex, when he saw Tory's panicked face.

Alex led Tory to the door, and shut it quickly behind

him. Then Tory heard the sound of something heavy
being dragged in front of the door. Tory turned around
and viewed the house. The inside was as dilapidated as the
outside. The paint was chipping, everything was covered in
a thick layer of dust, and a strong, musty, and awful scent
hung in the air.

Tory realized nobody had told him which room he
was supposed to sleep in. But as he moved up the stairs,
he saw the words "Do Not Enter" written in black chalk
on the door nearest to the top of the steps. This had to be
The Room.

Tory stepped slowly into the room and surveyed it
from left to right. He looked around to make sure none of
the kids were there waiting to jump out and scare him. He
checked everywhere in the room before sitting on the bed.
He looked out the window, it was getting dark fast, and
soon he would be alone at Betts farm.

He tried desperately to get to sleep before dark, but
it was impossible. Soon he was in pitch darkness, and all
the other kids were long gone to their nice, bright homes.
Only then did Tory notice what really good condition
compared to the rest of the house, the bed was in. Why
was that?

Tory was actually finding the farm pretty peaceful.
He was enjoying the sounds of the night animals, the
strong breeze, and the rattling of the trees. Tory soon
drifted off to sleep. He awoke sometime later and noticed
something very strange. Silence. He couldn't hear the
animals anymore, the wind had stopped, and there was
only complete silence. Tory tried to sit up and realized he

couldn't move his legs. His heart felt like it was going to beat out of his chest.

Whatever was happening had to be completely explainable. Tory didn't believe any ghost nonsense. He shut his eyes tightly until he had calmed down. When he opened them, he found he wasn't alone in the room.

Two bright eyes stared at him from the corner of the room. Fear gripped Tory. He tried to convince himself the eyes were only his imagination. He closed his eyes and opened them again. Now he could see that the eyes were inches from his face, and they had a body. The eyes belonged to a giant black dog with thick, coarse hair and sharp, bared fangs.

Tory's blood felt like ice as he tried to escape the bed, but he realized he couldn't move at all. His entire body was immobile from head to toe and he struggled to breathe. He accepted that he could do nothing but close his eyes and await his horrible fate.

After a few moments, Tory found that he was still alive. He opened his eyes; the horrible dog was gone. Now he could move, and gained control of his breathing. Not willing to risk encountering the beast again, Tory ran to the window and opened it. He quickly clambered out on the roof, shutting the window behind him. He sat there wide-awake until the first brightening of the sky meant it was almost sunrise.

He could see Alex and the rest of the kids coming down from the hill. He wasn't sure what they would say, or what would happen now, but he figured that this was the only time he would be happy to see Alex.

BIGFOOT

Do you ever feel overwhelmed by your phones, fax, email and everything else? How about a little camping trip in the mountains where you can get away from it all and enjoy nature? There is nothing like getting out into the wilds of West Virginia to go fishing or hiking or camping.

Now, when you head out, miles from civilization, to "Almost Heaven," you're likely to hear some crazy rumors from the locals. They like to tell stories about scary creatures. The one you'll worry about the most is about some kind of giant, hairy "Bigfoot" type creature they say roams the West Virginia woods. Don't pay those rumors any mind. You know how people like to talk. I can tell you that people think they see large dark shapes moving through the woods, but it's more than likely just shadows.

The light in these woods can play tricks on you. Relax and enjoy yourself.

There was a couple that insisted they saw a pair of eyes watching them through the trees while they were fishing. They said the eyes were eerily human, but surrounded by fur. They were sure it was Bigfoot.

The things people let themselves believe! There are

plenty of wild animals in the West Virginia woods it could have been. That's part of what attracts many people to come in the first place. That's just part of nature in all her glory.

There's nothing like it. You find an idyllic spot to make camp and set up some tents. Maybe a beautiful little open area surrounded by woods with a creek nearby. Once the work is done and you have set up camp, then you can cook something over the fire; maybe roast some marshmallows. You can sit around the campfire telling stories and enjoy the warmth and light of the fire.

But make sure the stories don't get you too scared to enjoy a good night's sleep under the stars. Especially as you let the fire wind down to coals. I don't want you to be one of those people who wake in a cold sweat with your heart racing, just because you heard a horrible deep screaming howl. Don't let yourself become someone who sits with their sleeping bag pulled up around them, afraid to move, because you hear something making horrible noises and moving heavily through the woods and bush.

When you think you hear something huge and heavy walking around outside of your tent, don't panic. You might think you see the shadow of a beast thrown across your tent. You might even be one of those people brave or fool enough to poke your head outside the tent, and come face to face with Bigfoot!

If by some chance you wake up in the morning and discover huge human-looking footprints around your tent and down by the creek, ... well, I don't know what to tell you. It's shocking how many people try to convince themselves that Bigfoot is alive and well and living in West Virginia, because they claim to have seen him. If you think you have run into Bigfoot, could you do me one favor? Don't spread it around, it's bad for business.

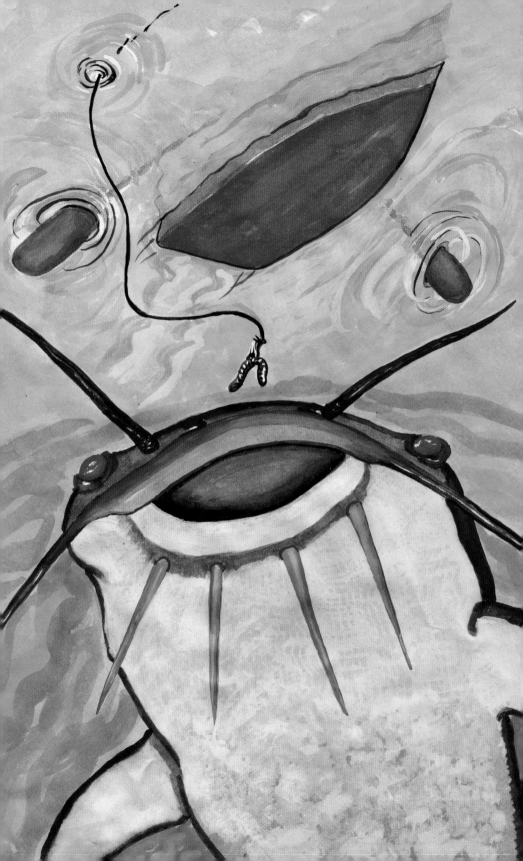

THE CATFISH MONSTER

Sam had had a rough week. A lot had happened, but he couldn't bear to think about any of it. Right now he was headed to the river to go fishing and that was all he was going to think about. He stepped carefully through the brush to get down to the riverbank where he'd left his boat. He flipped the boat over, cleared out the dirt and leaves, and pushed it into the water.

After loading his fishing gear in the boat, Sam stepped in, sat down and pushed away from the shore. He steadied the boat and paddled to his favorite spot right under the bridge in the shade. Not only was it comfortable, but the fish liked to feed there.

Sam casually cast his line just a few yards from the boat and let the bait sink. He placed his pole in a holder and kicked back. He loved fishing, but right now he didn't care if he caught anything or not. It was so relaxing and quiet here; he had needed it.

Suddenly there was a tug on his line and Sam jumped up to grab the pole. This had to be a big fish! It took a lot of his effort to reel it in. It was putting up a fight and Sam was thinking it was a carp or a catfish or maybe even a large bass. As it got closer, Sam could just start making out a fish on the end of the line. Then, a huge dark shape came up from beneath him, and grabbed the fish at the end of his line, and dove back down. The line sang out in a high-pitched whine as it was ripped through Sam's reel.

Without thinking Sam tightened his grip on his pole; before he knew it he was yanked overboard, smacking into the water. He ended up almost on top of the biggest creature you can imagine. He watched dumbstruck as fully thirty feet of giant catfish slid by underneath him. Then his stomach sank and his blood ran cold with terror as the beast turned toward him. It had bulging red eyes that fixed on him.

Sam dropped his pole and swam for his life, just managing to clamber onto the boat before the fish got to him. He thought he was safe in the boat, but to his surprise the fish turned and came back at him at full speed. The monster fish rammed the boat with such force that Sam was tossed in the air and went flying.

Maybe the only thing that saved him was the fact that he landed close enough to shore that he was able to get out of the water before the fish could turn around. Sam stood up and looked back out over the water. He caught just one more glimpse of the huge fish before it disappeared into the murky depths.

You know, Sam had heard tales all his life about monster fish. Many a fisherman will tell stories of giant fish and nobody ever believes them. People discount the stories with a wave of their hands. They chalk them up to being about "the one that got away" that are made up by the disgruntled fishermen who tell them. Now, after being "the fisherman who got away," Sam will have to wonder. Did he doze off and dream it? Or had some fishermen been telling the truth after all?

DEVIL'S TEA TABLES

Because of its geography, West Virginia is home to all kinds of beautiful, unusual rock formations. If you look, you might spot a formation that looks like a giant stone mushroom, with a narrow column of rock supporting a flat slab of rock on top of it. Some people think they look like giant tables. I suppose that's why they are commonly called tea tables. To be more exact, West Virginia folk call them "devil's tea tables."

It could be that people call these rock formations "devil's tea tables" because that's what they are. There are people who will swear that the devil himself visits them. You don't want to interrupt the devil when he is having tea, do you? Legend has it that when the devil is around a heavy mist will shroud the tea tables and hide the old bugger.

One day two men were traveling down the Elk River in a boat. It was a beautiful day and they had finished work, so they took their time. A magnificent tea table formation that they had often passed came into view. One of the men wanted to stop and hike up to it. Since they had time, the hiker's friend was happy to stop. He agreed to sit and wait with the boat.

When they reached the tea table, they saw that it was hidden by an odd mist that clung to it and nothing else. The man's partner didn't give the mist a second thought and jumped from the boat as soon as they got to shore. The one started scrambling up the slope, while the other sat back and kicked his feet up. He figured it would take his partner a half an hour or so to get there and back. The man waited and waited and waited.

Hours later his partner stumbled back down the hill, climbing into the boat without a word. His eyes were empty, devoid of life. He never recovered. He spent the rest of his life an empty shell of a man.

What the man who'd stayed behind did not know was that his partner had stumbled upon the devil himself. He had had the horrible misfortune of interrupting the devil having tea. The devil had loomed before him and looked at the man with cruel and merciless eyes. Then the devil had reached down and, with a mere pinch of his fingers, he pulled away the man's soul. He crumbled it up and sprinkled into his cup of tea like a bit of sugar. Then the devil waved the poor man away and returned to his tea.

This was not the first time someone unwittingly stumbled upon the devil, and it sure won't be the last. So take heed. If you see a devil's tea table, admire it from afar. If a mist surrounds it, look away and run!

THE FLATWOODS MONSTER

Jason stood at the foot of the woods. His family had just moved, and he wasn't happy about the new house. They had moved from New York, to Braxton County, West Virginia. There were no tall buildings, no taxis, and no big crowds walking the streets. It was always too quiet here.

Jason had made two friends here, Eddie and Freddie May, who along with their family had lived here their whole lives. But Jason was still sure he could never get used to the place.

Jason's new house sat at the edge of some deep woods. Animal calls, rustling leaves, and other sounds strange to Jason emanated from the woods day and night. His parents said it was peaceful and reminded them of their childhoods. Jason thought it was creepy. He could sleep through the familiar loud sounds of the city, but not these new ones. To him they sounded lonely and ominous.

Jason started school the next day, and was dreading it. His parents had told him not to complain, and that they were lucky his dad had found a job here. Eddie and

Freddie had told him that on the first day of school the kids usually told stories of what adventures they'd had over the summer. Jason was sure he had nothing to tell except he hated this place, and he couldn't say that!

Jason waited at the edge of the woods for his friends. They were late. Freddie and Eddie had promised to take him on a hike through the woods and show him around. Although he would never say it aloud, Jason had never felt comfortable in the woods. He hadn't wanted to go, but he didn't want to explain why, so he accepted.

When Eddie and Freddie arrived, they told Jason that there had been a change in plans. He had been invited over to their house for a cookout on the grill. Jason was greatly relieved to hear this and gladly walked with them back to their house. When they arrived, Eddie and Freddie's mother Kathleen had already started cooking.

"Hello Jason!" Mrs. May greeted warmly. "We decided to welcome you to the neighborhood with a cookout."

"Thank you very much," Jason replied.

Jason played in the yard with the kids for a while until suddenly something breached the cloud line. The kids stopped and stared at the sky with their mouths open, in awe as a giant metallic disk flew overhead. Its multicolored lights flashed in brilliant colors as it appeared to crash in a cloud of dirt on the hill in the woods.

The boys yelled for their mom and Jason stood shaking. Mrs. May came rushing to the back yard in the dark, flashlight in hand. "For goodness sakes children, what happened?"

The three boys described what they had seen to Mrs. May, and her eyes widened as they pointed to the spot where the saucer had crashed. The boys decided they had to investigate. Mrs. May led the way with the flashlight until the group came across the ship.

A large section of the woods was lit with a strange light. They smelled a strange metallic odor, and their eyes burned. Suddenly, a loud thumping noise came from the ship, followed by some sort of hissing. Oil splattered all over Mrs. May and the children.

Next they heard another sound coming from the woods; its source was apparently close-by. When Mrs. May turned her flashlight towards the noise, their jaws dropped. They saw some sort of creature floating just above the ground. Two bright, white light beams came from its eyes, way up high. The thing was at least twelve feet tall with some kind of green clothing, hanging down in folds. It's bright red face stood out against some kind of hood, which was shaped like an ace of spades.

Mrs. May and the children gasped in horror as the figure turned from his ship and began to approach them. Without a word to each other, Mrs. May and the children turned and ran through the woods faster than they ever had before. They didn't stop until they came to the house, where they ran inside and locked the door. Mrs. May called the police while the terrified children stared out the windows.

Jason was still in shock. He shook with fear, knowing he'd be unable to sleep tonight. What was that horrible creature? Would it come back for them? Where was it from? One thing he did know: he had his story for school.

THE GREENBRIER GHOST

Zona Heaster was one of the town beauties at only 15, the same age she first met Edward Shue. A big, muscular, imposing man, the newcomer was considered very handsome. For Edward and Zona, it was pretty much love at first sight, and Edward wanted to get married right away. Edward quickly got Zona alone and way from her parents, and convinced her to run away with him to get married that very evening. It was a November evening in the year of 1896 when they married. They soon moved into a nice house of their own. It seemed like a romantic start to a perfect life for Zona, but that was not to be.

Only two short months after the wedding, a neighbor boy named Anderson Jones found Zona Heaster Shue dead. Edward had been working out of town and sent the boy to check on Zona. The poor Jones boy had found the girl lying at the foot of the stairs: her face frozen in a horrible death grimace, her body already gone stiff and cold. Shortly thereafter Zona was declared dead of natural causes. Her body was taken to her family home and buried in the family cemetery.

Here is where the tragedy may have ended, but it didn't. Zona's mother, Mary Heaster, insisted that Zona's ghost had begun appearing to her. Somehow Zona appeared four times, each time revealing to Mary precise details about her home and family details that Mary had no way of knowing. Ms. Heaster was very convincing as she recanted detail after detail about the home where Zona had spent the last two months of her life.

Zona finally revealed to her mother the truth about how she died. It was at the hands of her murderous husband, Edward Shue. How he had taken her small neck in his huge strong hands and broke it. Zona told here mother how Edward had put a dress with a high stiff collar on her, and tied several scarves around her neck to hide his crime.

Mary Heaster was utterly convinced. So convinced that she persuaded the sheriff to dig up Zona's body. Once they did, it was quickly apparent that everything Zona's ghost had told her mother was true. Edward Shue had taken Zona's neck in his large hands, and snapped it like a twig.

There the poor girl lay in the dress with the high neck all tied up with the scarves just like she had described. An autopsy proved that she had died from a badly broken neck!

Edward Shue was arrested, tried, and convicted for murdering his wife. He is the only man in this country ever to have been convicted in a court of law based on the testimony of a ghost!

Who says the dead can't speak?

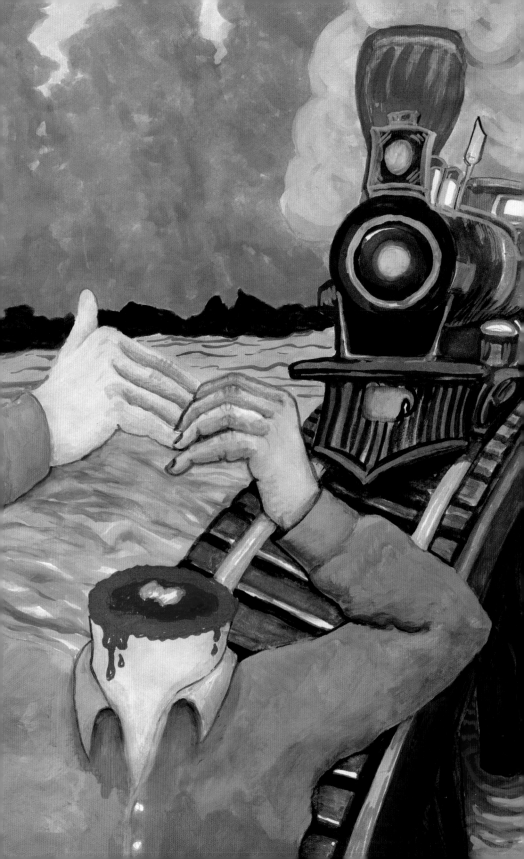

THE HEADLESS MAN OF FAYETTE COUNTY

I don't remember how I got here. I wake up and find myself walking on railroad tracks, tracks I know quite well. I've walked the tracks between Pax and Weirwood many times, and everything around me is familiar. I just don't remember anything about why I'm here now.

I feel like I woke from a dream, only to find myself trapped in an endless loop of some other endless dream. I can't seem to make myself step away from the tracks or turn around or sit down. I just keep stumbling along, feeling the rails and gravel under my boots. Then I remember I'm looking for something. I can't for the life of me recall what it is, but I know that it's important. I've lost something extremely important and that's why I'm here.

"Think, think, think!" I mutter to myself. My mind is in a fog. A bridge is just ahead. An ominous feeling creeps over me. I trudge on along the track searching desperately this way and that as I start across the bridge.

The track begins to rumble and shake. A thunderous noise surrounds me. All of a sudden, a train appears out of nowhere; it is right on top of me, and moving at full speed.

This bridge I'm on is narrow, and there is no place to go but over the edge.

As I turn to make my leap, my foot slips. I begin tumbling through the air, falling head over heels. As my body plunges into the river below, my memory comes rushing back. I've been through this before. I remember the train rushing at me, the noise so loud I cover my ears as I leap off of the bridge. When I slipped, I fell straight onto the tracks and the train cleanly severs my head, sending it tumbling in another direction. By the time I hit the water my head is gone.

At least now I remember what it was I lost. I've been out here all this time trying to find my head! I know I won't rest until I find it.

If you are ever traveling through these parts, especially if you are walking along the train tracks over the river, I'd appreciate it if you would keep an eye out for my head. If you find it, set it up by the bridge. I'll come along soon enough looking for it like I always do. You can even just wait there and hand it to me as I stumble along. Then, I could quit being the headless man of Fayette County and get some rest.

MEN IN BLACK

On the fringes of strange happenings, of UFO sightings and alien encounters, stands another kind of mysterious figure, the dark and unexplained Men In Black.

Said to visit and often threaten witnesses who have seen UFO's or aliens, these strange men may seem more ominous than the aliens themselves. They demand that witnesses keep quiet about what they have experienced.

The Men In Black or MIB's are thought to be part of some secret government agency. They are sometimes portrayed as "damage control." It's their job to contain, subdue and stifle information about aliens and UFO's from getting out to the public.

People who have had direct contact with the men, however, paint a very different picture. Witnesses describe these Men In Black (if they are men at all) as being bald and very pale, lacking eyebrows and eyelashes. Their lips are bright red, which is startling against their white skin. Dressed in black business suits with black ties, shoes and hats with white shirts, at first glance they look like somber businessmen.

MIB's are said to behave oddly. One witness said he met an MIB that didn't seem to know what a ballpoint

pen was, or how to use it. Once he was shown how the pen worked, he was delighted and played with the pen for hours. What makes the story more odd is that the MIB's are usually spotted carrying extremely sophisticated, high-tech gadgets of their own.

Hundreds of people claim to have met these strange men, but nobody knows much about them. One woman claimed that the MIB's erased part of her memory. Who ever heard of that happening?

THE MOTHMAN

It started in the fall of 1966. In the small town of Clendenin, West Virginia, five men in a cemetery were digging a grave when they saw it: something brown, shaped like a human with wings flying over them. Their shocking report traveled quickly through the sleepy town. Excitement rippled through the community and gave everyone something new to talk about. What did the men see, or think they saw? Had they really seen anything at all? Opinions and explanations were as varied as the people telling the story.

The excitement would have died down considerably sooner and the whole incident might have almost been forgotten, but the story didn't end there. Only a few days later "the creature" made another appearance, and this time he really showed itself. Two couples looking for a secluded spot for romance ended up in the abandoned World War II TNT plant near Point Pleasant. They got the surprise of their lives when the creature showed up. At first he stayed far enough away that they could only see his large, red glowing eyes. But he came closer. He came right up on them, so close that they could describe him perfectly.

He did not have a typical neck and head. His eyes sat at the top of what we would consider his chest. His large wings were near the eye area, but attached to his back, and they said he stood about seven feet tall. Worse, he chased these terrified young people all the way back to town, flying at speeds in excess of one hundred miles an hour to keep up with them in their car. He reportedly often flew at high speeds. Did he like to show off?

Turns out the sheriff in town knew these young people and considered them honest kids. Their reputations plus their real terror when they burst in his office convinced him. He believed their story.

News of the latest sighting spread like wildfire. By now the creature had been dubbed the "Mothman." Some people went out looking for him. Others, more fearful folk, tried to stay inside, especially at night. Even the most dubious still found themselves keeping an eye out.

Perhaps the Mothman tried to stay out of sight, but he was still spotted many times over the following year.

Then came the tragedy. The Silver Bridge, connecting Point Pleasant, West Virginia and Gallipolis, Ohio, collapsed, sending dozens of car plunging through the darkness into the river below. Forty-six people were killed. After the bridge collapsed, the Mothman seemed to disappear.

Many people think the creature was connected somehow to the collapse of the bridge. Some believe he had something to do with causing its collapse. Others say he was trying to warn people of the collapse.

The truth of the matter is that he was not supposed to let himself be seen. He's in big trouble for that. As for the rest of the truth, well, you know how the saying goes, if I told you I'd have to kill you. It's best kept a mystery.

THE OGUA WATER MONSTER

Human beings are smelly, noisy and unpredictable creatures. They're dangerous 'cause you just never know when they're going to turn on you. Here we go again! The adults love to float around telling their stories of close encounters with humans.

We've grown up on these far-fetched tales. But whether you believe the stories or not, we all come swimming when Uncle Birke starts talking. Uncle Birke is the biggest, toughest and by far, the coolest Ogua there is. His spines are long, his skin is thick and tough and he has a bunch of really amazing scars.

And, he always has the best stories. He is fearless. Instead of swimming away, when he happens upon a human on the riverbank or in shallow water, Uncle Birke hunts them. He says he has grabbed quite a few unsuspecting humans in his big jaws and carried them down into the deep waters to drown them. "I can't say as I recommend eating them though," he says "they taste bad and their bones are tough."

As a rule we ogua are supposed to steer clear of

humans. The very young are strictly forbidden from leaving the deepest and safest areas of the river. Since I am a little older, my friends and I are allowed to go a lot closer to the shallows, but we're still forbidden to go near the shore. I used to think all the human stories were made up to scare the younger ogua away from the more dangerous parts of the river. My friends and I used to argue about whether or not humans really existed.

That all changed this morning. My friends and I were swimming around and half-heartedly hunting for fish. We started daring one another to go further into the shallows than we were supposed to. Next thing you know, we were swimming within sight of the shore and feeling pretty pleased with ourselves. That's when we heard the screeching sound that stung our ears and sent shivers down our spines. It was like nothing we had heard before. Most of my friends exchanged glances with their eyes wide with fear; and then took off for the safety of the deep waters and home as fast as they could go.

My best friend Fred and I stayed. We looked at each other and knew we were thinking the same thing ... humans! This was our chance to see a human for ourselves and there was no way we were going back. Right then the smell hit us. It's hard to describe that smell but it made our stomachs roll and we had to resist the urge to swim to fresher water. Fred and I gave each other a look and then swam toward the surface and closer to the shore. As we reached the air line we pushed our heads up and let just our eyes lift out of the water.

There on the bank of the river stood three of the

49

ugliest and most horrifying creatures you could imagine. They were pink and pulpy looking with huge legs and they were standing up on their rear legs. Their heads were egg shaped and attached with skinny necks. My spines stood on end and my mouth dropped open. I felt a tug on my tail and realized it was Fred pulling on me, trying to get me to leave. I dove down and Fred and I took off swimming as fast as we could. We were all pumped up with adrenaline. I can't believe it! Humans are real and we saw them! As we headed for home, I couldn't help but wonder if they taste as bad as Uncle Birke says.

THE THUNDERBIRD OF OWL HEAD MOUNTAIN

Ten-year-old Landy Junkins was used to running
errands for her folks. On a cold winter day she made
her way through the snow to check on old Mrs. Warnick
who lived a couple of miles away. It was February 1895.
Landy's toes and fingers were starting to hurt, but she
pushed on. She started through the large frozen field
ahead of her, but she never made it to the other side.
Landy never made it to Mrs. Warnick's place, nor did she
ever make it home. She was never seen again.

Everyone went out looking for the young girl, but all
their searching turned up was a lone set of small footprints
that went out into the middle of a large frozen field and
stopped.

This tragedy would be only the beginning of the
horror stories coming from Owl Head Mountain during
this long, hard winter. Not far from the field where Landy
disappeared, a farmer named Hance Hardrick had put
up a shed to shelter his sheep through the bad weather.
When he went out to check on the sheep he found one
sheep missing, with a large hole ripped through the roof

of the shed. There were no footprints in the snow but the farmer's own. Whatever did the damage had to be able to fly, and it had to be big enough to carry off a full-grown sheep!

Only a few days later, Deputy Sheriff Nihiser and his son would become the first people to actually see the beast. They were tracking a deer through the woods when they heard the pitiful screams of a doe. The two men were stunned when they came upon the scene. A giant bird was attacking the doe. The deer fought desperately to save her fawn, but she was just no match for the huge talons and monstrous beak of the giant bird. The bird stood taller than a man and had an enormous wingspan. It scooped up the screaming fawn and flew away, leaving the torn up doe with her eyes pecked out. The hunters escaped unnoticed and unharmed but the next hunter to meet this winged nightmare was not so lucky.

Peter Swadley was out hunting with his favorite dog, Gunner. Out of nowhere he was attacked in a flurry of great huge wings. Giant claws ripped at him and a giant beak smashed against his head like an axe. Gunner ran at the bird and attacked it from behind. The bird let go of Peter and went after the dog. Gunner saved his owner but could not save himself. Peter watched helplessly as Gunner was carried away in the bird's talons. A neighbor found Peter and got him to a doctor. He may be the only man who can say he survived an attack by the Thunderbird of Owl Head Mountain.

UFO's

West Virginia is a hotbed of UFO activity. People have been reporting UFO's for as long as anyone can remember. Sometimes they show up in swarms like they did for almost a year around Sistersville between 1896 and 1897. Lots of people report seeing the same UFO's night after night. Other times it's a lone craft appearing to just one person. Some witnesses report flying saucers and just as often witnesses report long cylindrical flying objects.

UFO's project powerful beams of light and flash red, green and white lights. Supposedly they are bright, shiny, metallic airships that can hover without moving or making a sound. Then, they can suddenly shoot off at mind-numbing speeds.

A lot of people, like me, just see lights in the sky. Lights burned forever in my memory. I saw them on a perfect summer night. A handful of us kids were outside lying on our backs watching the night sky. We pointed out satellites that we could see gliding along their orbits and we raced to identify different types of planes or helicopters.

Once in a while on a summer night you'd see a falling star. That was the most exciting, and it's what we hoped to see. One night we watched a light that seemed red one minute, then green or white the next. At first we thought it was an odd star. When it started moving we figured it was some type of plane but it didn't make any noise.

All of a sudden it shot across the entire sky in a sweeping arc. Then it did something even crazier. It stopped dead still. Just sat there winking at us like a star again. But then that crazy light started flying patterns in the sky that were impossible. Full speed 180-degree direction changes, zigzags, and triangles traced out across a huge span of sky. We had to move our heads back and forth to follow it.

We were excited and entertained at first. But slowly it hit us that this thing wasn't of this world. It wasn't man-made and it was no natural part of the night sky. The longer we watched it, the more we started to become afraid. What if it landed? What if it could shoot death rays? It had to be aliens! Then it took off and disappeared. We were left to wonder what we had just seen. Was it just our imaginations? Or was it one more UFO visiting the night skies of West Virginia.

VEGGIE MAN

I'm a gardening freak. Morning, noon or night you can catch me out weeding, or planting, or deadheading something in the garden. Sometimes when the weather is perfect, I like to go out and sit with my plants all around me and take in their beauty and sweet smells. It was on just such an evening that I encountered ... well, I don't know what "it" was.

I had knelt down between two rows of sunflowers to pull some weeds when movement caught my eye. When I looked toward the movement, I could just make out what looked to be a great tall plant behind the row of flowers. It towered over me. My sunflowers are six to ten feet tall, and this plant was right up there with them. I'd say at least seven feet tall with a stalk so big you couldn't reach around it with both hands.

I leaned a little this way and that trying to get a better look at it. It had as far as I could tell, only two odd long branches that hung straight down along its stalk and ended with fingery vines and tendrils. This was not like anything I had ever seen before.

I broke out in a light sweat as my mind raced. Giant plants don't just appear. I couldn't come up with any reasonable explanation for this strange plant appearing in my garden. It gave me the creeps. I shivered.

I wanted to get a better look but I had to get up my nerve. Finally, I took a deep breath and stood up. As I started moving toward the plant there was a flurry of movement. All the sunflowers shook, and that strange plant started moving. The lower part of its great stalk separated into legs and it walked in long strides with its two odd branches swinging like arms.

In a flash, it dashed to the edge of the woods that bordered the garden. But before it disappeared, it paused for a moment and stared at me with two big, gold unblinking eyes. Then, it was gone.

My knees felt wobbly and my legs weak. I was definitely shaken, but I stood there for the longest time not believing what I had just seen. Eventually I went inside and I did what anyone would do; I looked it up on the internet (well, you never know).

Turns out there was a guy named Jennings Frederick that reported seeing something like this years ago. He called it the "Vegetable Man," and was sure it was some type of alien. I don't know if it was an alien or not. I just know it almost scared me out of the garden for good. I'd be happy if it never comes back.

WEST VIRGINIA BOOK COMPANY

Specializing in books about West Virginia

If you enjoyed *Monsters and Ghost of West Virginia*, you may be interested in other books about ghost, folklore, and monsters in the mountain state. Below is a partial list of some of our favorite supernatural titles:

The Greenbrier Ghost and other Strange Stories Volumes 1-2 by Dennis Deitz

The Devil's Tea Tables: West Virginia Ghost Tales and Other Stories by Mack Samples

Elk River Ghosts: Tales and Lore by Mack Samples

Mothman: Behind the Red Eyes by Jeff Wamsley

Mothman: The Facts Behind the Legend by Jeff Wamsley

Cry of the Banshee: History and Hauntings of West Virginia and the Ohio Valley by Susan Sheppard

For a complete list of West Virginia ghost books and ordering information, please visit us at *www.wvbookco.com*

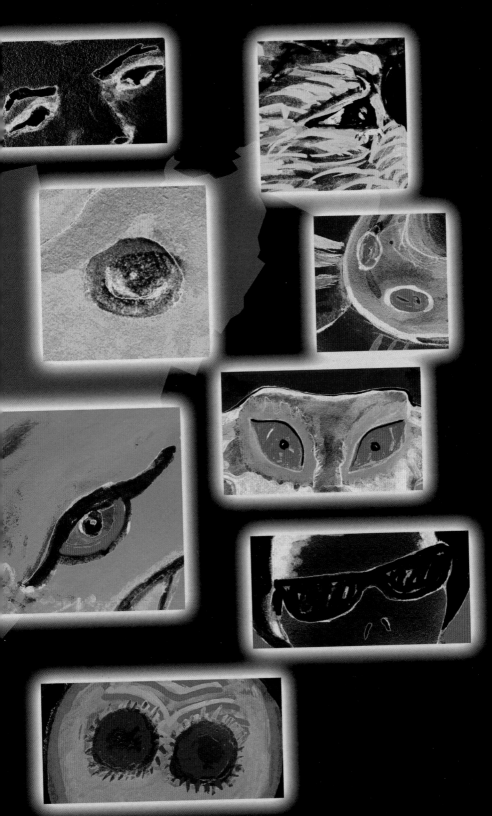